by
Pamela Conn Beall
and
Susan Hagen Nipp

Illustrated by
Nancy Spence Klein

PRICE STERN SLOAN
Los Angeles

To Nancy —
A special person, a special friend

A special thank you to Barry, Mauri and the Wee Singers

Published by Price Stern Sloan, Inc.
11150 Olympic Boulevard, Suite 650
Los Angeles, California 90064

15 14 13 12 11 10 9 8 7 6

ISBN: 0-8431-2760-0

PREFACE

“Frog went a-courtin’ and he did ride, m, hm.” Or is it “A froggie went a-courtin’ and he did ride, uh, huh”? Or maybe “Mister Frog...” Which way is correct? They all are, of course, because folk songs are songs of the people that have passed down from generation to generation, changing slightly with each new singer and each new situation.

An integral part of our history, folk music helps us to know and understand our forefathers. We can enjoy their humor and imagination, experience their wonderful storytelling and learn about their customs, activities, interests and emotions.

Children delight in singing these songs today, just as they did decades or even centuries ago. As you sing with them, perhaps you can add to the continual change of folk music when you say, “But I remember it this way...”

Enjoy!

Pam Beall
Susan Nipp

TABLE OF CONTENTS

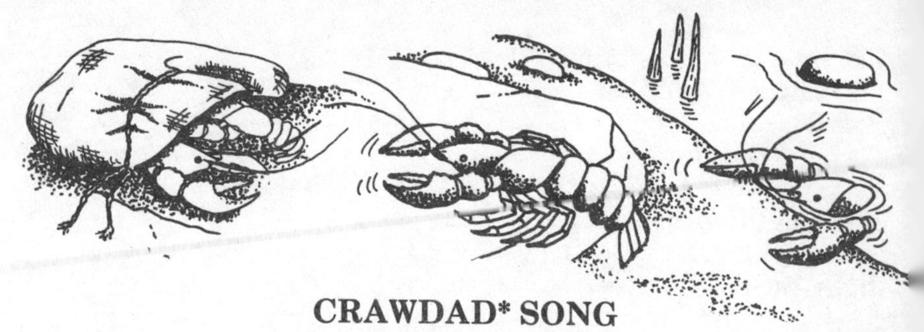

CRAWDAD* SONG

Southern

2. Sittin' on the bank 'til my feet get cold, Honey,
   Sittin' on the bank 'til my feet get cold, Babe,
   Sittin' on the bank 'til my feet get cold,
   Lookin' down that crawdad hole,
   Honey, Baby mine.
3. Yonder comes a man with a sack on his back, Honey...
   Packin' all the crawdads he can pack...
4. The man fell down and he broke that sack, Honey...
   See those crawdads backing back...
5. I heard the duck say to the drake, Honey...
   There ain't no crawdads in this lake...

* looks like a small lobster (also called crayfish)

BOUGHT ME A CAT

Southern

3. Bought me a duck and the duck pleased me,
   I fed my duck under yonder tree.
 *Duck goes quack, quack,
   Hen goes chimmy-chuck, chimmy-chuck,
 Cat goes fiddle-i-fee.
4. . . .goose goes hissy, hissy . . .
5. . . .sheep goes baa, baa . . .
6. . . .pig goes oink, oink . . .
7. . . .cow goes moo, moo . . .
8. . . .horse goes neigh, neigh . . .
9. . . .dog goes bow-wow, bow-wow . . .

POLLY WOLLY DOODLE

Southern

1. Oh, I went down South for to see my Sal, Sing
Pol-ly wol-ly doo-dle all the day, My Sal, she is a
spunk-y gal, Sing Pol-ly wol-ly doo-dle all the day.

Chorus
Fare thee well, fare thee well, Fare thee well my
fair-y fay, For I'm goin' to Lou'-si-an-a for to
see my Su-sy-an-na, Sing Pol-ly wol-ly doo-dle all the day.

2. Oh, my Sal, she is a maiden fair,
Sing Polly wolly doodle all the day,
With curly eyes and laughing hair,
Sing Polly wolly doodle all the day.
Chorus

3. Behind the barn, down on my knees...
I thought I heard a chicken sneeze...
Chorus

. He sneezed so hard with the whooping cough...
He sneezed his head and tail right off...
Chorus
. Oh, a grasshopper sittin' on a railroad track...
A-pickin' his teeth with a carpet tack...
Chorus
. Oh, I went to bed but it wasn't any use...
My feet stuck out like a chicken roost...
Chorus
Optional Descant
S.N.
F
1. Oh, I went down South to see my Sal, I'm
C7
sing-ing all the way, My — Sal, she is a
F
spunk-y gal, I'm sing-ing all the day.
Chorus
C7
Fare thee well, Fare thee well, Fare thee well, I say,
F
Fare thee well, Fare thee well, Sing-ing all the day.

SHORT'NIN' BREAD
Plantation Song
C
F
C
F
C
1. Three lit-tle chil-dren, ly-in' in bed, Two were sick and the
G7
C
oth-er 'most dead. Sent for the doc-tor and the
F
C
F
C
G7
C
doc-tor said, "Give those chil-dren some short-'nin' breac
Chorus
Ma-ma's lit-tle ba-by loves short-'nin', short-'nin',
F
C
G7
C
Ma-ma's lit-tle ba-by loves short-'nin' bread,

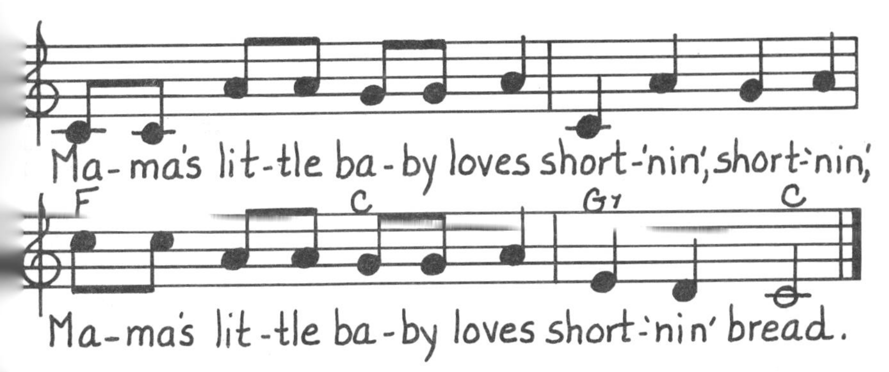

2. Put on the skillet, slip on the lid,
   Mama's gonna make a little short'nin' bread.
   That ain't all she's gonna do,
   Mama's gonna make a little coffee, too.
   Chorus
3. When those children, sick in bed,
   Heard that talk about short'nin' bread,
   Popped up well to dance and sing,
   Skipped around and cut the pigeon wing.*
   Chorus

Suggestion: Try a stamp/clap/stamp/clap pattern on the chorus.

* a frontier dance

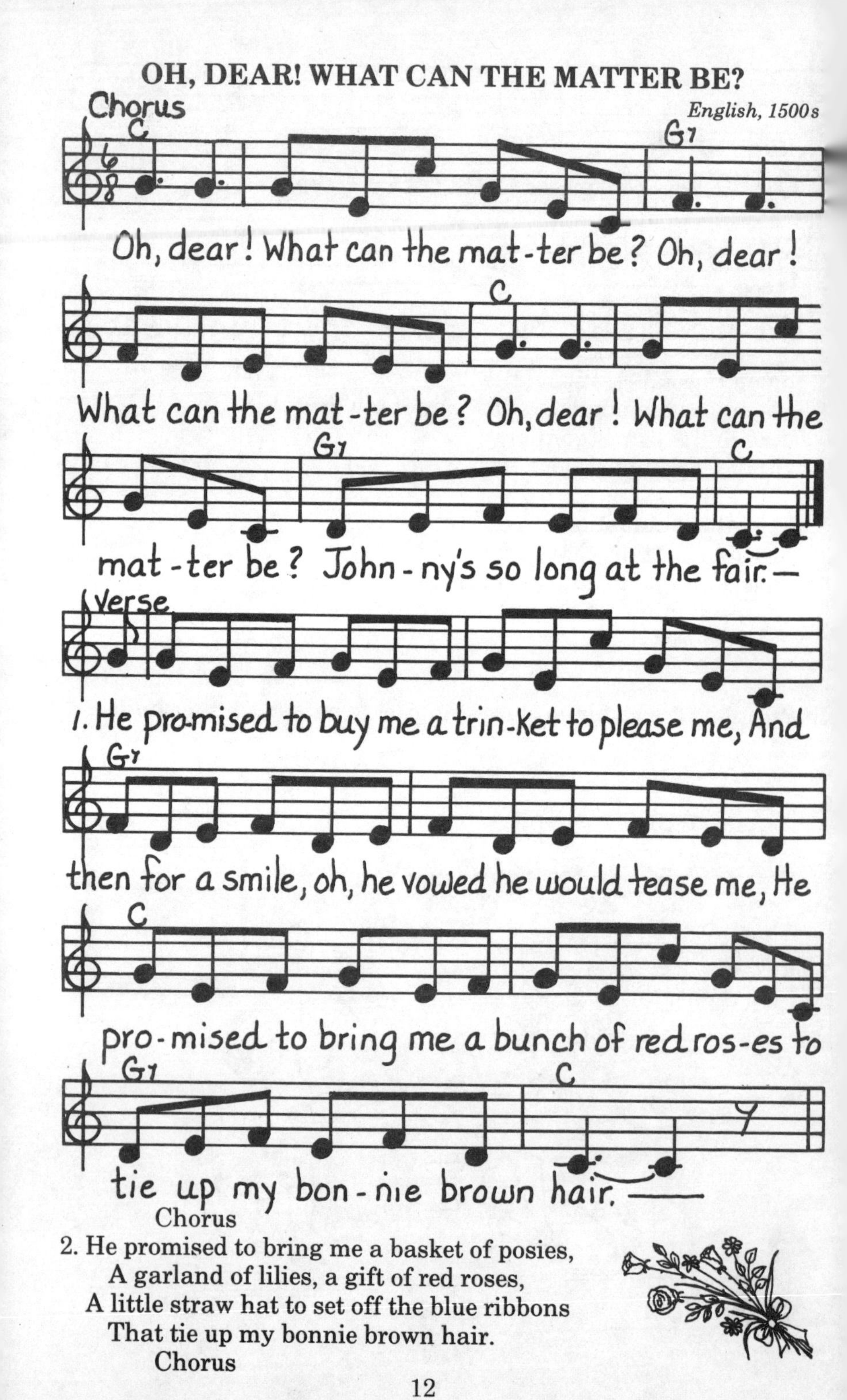
OH, DEAR! WHAT CAN THE MATTER BE?
Chorus
English, 1500s
C
G7
Oh, dear! What can the mat-ter be? Oh, dear!
C
What can the mat-ter be? Oh, dear! What can the
G7
C
mat-ter be? Johnny's so long at the fair.—
Verse
1. He promised to buy me a trin-ket to please me, And
G7
then for a smile, oh, he vowed he would tease me, He
C
pro-mised to bring me a bunch of red ros-es to
G7
C
tie up my bon-nie brown hair.—
Chorus
2. He promised to bring me a basket of posies,
A garland of lilies, a gift of red roses,
A little straw hat to set off the blue ribbons
That tie up my bonnie brown hair.
Chorus

THERE'S A LITTLE WHEEL A-TURNIN'

Spiritual

2. There's a[e] little song a-singin' in my[b] heart,
   There's a[e] little song a-singin' in my[b] heart,
In my[c] heart,[d]— in my[c] heart,[d]—
   There's a[e] little song a singin' in my[b] heart.
3. Oh, I[f] feel so very happy in my[b] heart...

Motions:

[a] Roll hands
[b] Form heart with hands (wrists together, fingernails touching)
[c] Hands over heart
[d] Hands out front, palms up
[e] Cup hands around mouth
[f] Clap

JENNIE JENKINS

2. Will you wear blue, Oh my dear, Oh my dear?
   Will you wear blue, Jennie Jenkins?
   No, I won't wear blue 'cause blue won't do,
   I'll buy me a fol-de-rol-dy, til-de-tol-dy, seek-a-double,
   Use-a-cause-a, roll-a-find-me, roll,
   Jennie Jenkins, roll.
3. Will you wear red...
   No, I won't wear red, it's the color of my head...
4. Will you wear pink...
   No, I won't wear pink, I'd rather drink ink...

5. Will you wear green...
   No, I won't wear green, it's the color of a bean...
6. Will you wear rose...
   No, I won't wear rose, it's the color of my nose...

Suggestions:
1. With a group of children, have those stand up who are wearing the color about which you are singing.
2. Use hand motions on the following:
   buy me a - tap knees twice
   fol-de-rol-dy - clap twice
   til-de-tol-dy - tap knees twice
   seek a double - clap twice
   use-a-cause-a - tap knees twice
   roll-a-find-me - clap twice
   roll - roll hands around each other
   Jennie Jenkins - clap three times
   roll - roll hands

THE WABASH CANNONBALL

Hobo Balla

2. Our eastern states are dandy, so the people always say,
From New York to St. Louis and Chicago by the way,
Through the hills of Minnesota where the rippling waters fall,
No chances can be taken on the Wabash Cannonball.
Chorus

The Wabash Cannonball was a legendary train of hobo folklore. It was 700 cars long and often arrived at its destination before leaving its starting point. It traveled so fast that one day it flew off the tracks into the sky and is still thought to be rushing through space.

GRIZZLY BEAR*

Southern Work Song

2. Well, my mama was a-scared of that grizzly bear,
   My mama was a-scared of that grizzly bear.
   So my Daddy went a-huntin' for that grizzly bear,
   My Daddy went a-huntin' for that grizzly bear.
3. He had long, long hair that grizzly bear...
   He had big, blue eyes that grizzly bear...
4. Well, he looked everywhere for that grizzly bear...
   But he couldn't find that great big grizzly bear...
5. So my mama's not a-scared of that grizzly bear...
   That great big grizzly, grizzly bear...

* This song is also sung as a call/response. Leader sings all but "grizzly bear" which chorus sings each time with enthusiasm.

TRAIN IS A-COMIN' *

Spiritual

2. Better get your ticket, oh, yes,
   Better get your ticket, oh, yes,
  Better get your ticket, better get your ticket,
   Better get your ticket, oh, yes.
3. Room for many more, oh, yes. . .
4. Train is a-leavin', oh, yes. . .

* This song is also sung as a call/response. Leader sings "Train is a-comin'." Response is "Oh, yes."

THE RATTLIN' BOG

Irish

Chorus

2. Now on that tree there was a branch,
 A rare branch and a rattlin' branch,
 And the branch on the tree
 And the tree in the bog
 And the bog down in the valley-o.
 Chorus

3. Now on that branch there was a limb,
 A rare limb and a rattlin' limb,
 And the limb on the branch
 And the branch on the tree
 And the tree in the bog
 And the bog down in the valley-o.
 Chorus

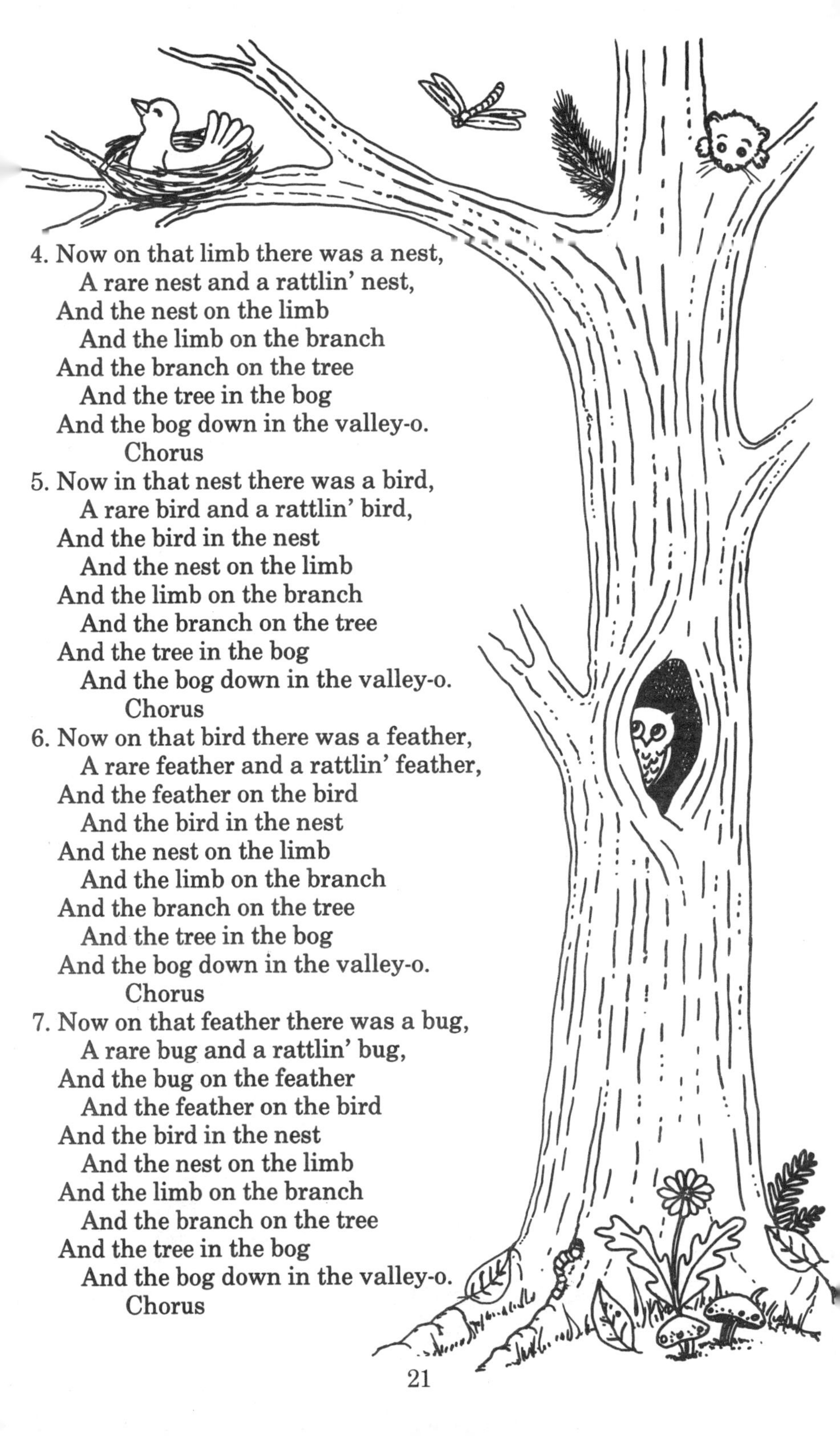

4. Now on that limb there was a nest,
   A rare nest and a rattlin' nest,
   And the nest on the limb
   And the limb on the branch
   And the branch on the tree
   And the tree in the bog
   And the bog down in the valley-o.
   Chorus
5. Now in that nest there was a bird,
   A rare bird and a rattlin' bird,
   And the bird in the nest
   And the nest on the limb
   And the limb on the branch
   And the branch on the tree
   And the tree in the bog
   And the bog down in the valley-o.
   Chorus
6. Now on that bird there was a feather,
   A rare feather and a rattlin' feather,
   And the feather on the bird
   And the bird in the nest
   And the nest on the limb
   And the limb on the branch
   And the branch on the tree
   And the tree in the bog
   And the bog down in the valley-o.
   Chorus
7. Now on that feather there was a bug,
   A rare bug and a rattlin' bug,
   And the bug on the feather
   And the feather on the bird
   And the bird in the nest
   And the nest on the limb
   And the limb on the branch
   And the branch on the tree
   And the tree in the bog
   And the bog down in the valley-o.
   Chorus

GREAT GRANDDAD

Cowboy

2. Twenty-one children came to bless
   The old man's home in the wilderness,
They slept on the floor with the dogs and the cats,
   And they hunted in the woods in their coonskin caps.
3. Great Granddad was a busy man,
   Cooked his grub in a frying pan,
He picked his teeth with his hunting knife,
   And he wore the same suit all his life.

BILLY BOY

English

2. Did she ask you to come in, Billy Boy, Billy Boy,
Did she ask you to come in, charming Billy?
Yes, she asked me to come in, there's a dimple in her chin,
She's a young thing and cannot leave her mother.
3. Can she make a cherry pie, Billy Boy, Billy Boy,
Can she make a cherry pie, charming Billy?
She can make a cherry pie, quick as a cat can wink an eye,
She's a young thing and cannot leave her mother.
4. How old is she, Billy Boy, Billy Boy,
How old is she, charming Billy?
Three times six and four times seven, twenty-eight and eleven,
She's a young thing and cannot leave her mother.

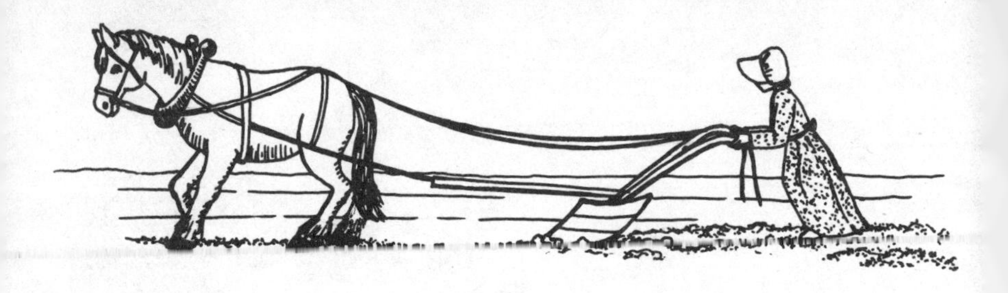

FATHER GRUMBLE

New England

2. "But you must milk the Tiny cow
For fear she should go dry,
And you must feed the little pigs
That are within the sty,
And you must watch the speckled hen
Or she will run away,
And you must wind the reel of yarn
That I spun yesterday."

3. The old woman took the staff in her hand
And went to drive the plow,
The old man took the pail in his hand
And went to milk the cow.
But Tiny hinched and Tiny flinched
And Tiny wrinkled her nose,
And Tiny gave the man such a kick
That the blood ran down to his toes.

4. 'Twas, "Hey, my good cow," and "Ho, my good cow,"
And "Now, my good cow, stand still.
If ever I milk this cow again,
'Twill be against my will."
He went to feed the little pigs
That stand in yonder sty,
He bumped his head against the post
And how the blood did fly.

5. And then he watched the speckled hen
For fear she'd run away,
But he forgot the reel of yarn
His wife spun yesterday.
He swore by all the leaves on the tree
And all the stars in heaven,
That his wife could do more work in a day
Than he could do in seven.

HOLD ON

2. Keep on plowin' and don't you tire,
   Ev'ry row goes higher and higher,
   Keep your hand on that plow,
   Hold on, hold on, hold on.
      Chorus
3. If you want to get to heaven, I'll tell you how,
   Keep your hand on the Gospel plow...
      Chorus
4. If that plow stays in your hand,
   Head you straight for the Promised Land...
      Chorus

THE OLD GRAY MARE

Adapted Spiritual

2. The old gray mare, she kicked on the whiffletree*,
   Kicked on the whiffletree, kicked on the whiffletree,
   The old gray mare, she kicked on the whiffletree,
   Many long years ago.
   Many long years ago, many long years ago,
   The old gray mare, she kicked on the whiffletree,
   Many long years ago.

* crossbar at the front of a wagon to which the harness strings are attached

THE BIG ROCK CANDY MOUNTAINS

Hobo Ballad

"The Big Rock Candy Mountains" is a hobo folk song about a legendary land that existed only in the hobo's imagination.

2. In the Big Rock Candy Mountains,
   You never change your socks,
   And little streams of lemonade
   Come a-tricklin' down the rocks,
   The hobos there are friendly
   And their fires all burn bright,
   There's a lake of stew and soda, too,
   You can paddle all around 'em in a big canoe
   In the Big Rock Candy Mountains.
   Chorus

CINDY

Appalachian

2. The first time that I saw her,
   She was standin' in the door,
   Her shoes and stockings in her hand,
   Her feet all over the floor.
      Chorus
3. I wish I was an apple
   A-hangin' on a tree,
   And every time my Cindy passed,
   She'd take a bite of me.
      Chorus

OLD JOE CLARK

2. I went down to Old Joe's house,
   Stayed to have some supper,
   Stubbed my toe on the table leg
   And stuck my nose in the butter.
      Chorus
3. Raccoon has a bushy tail,
   'Possum's tail is bare,
   Rabbit has no tail at all,
   'Cept a bunch of hair.
      Chorus

A FROG WENT A-COURTIN'

2. He rode up to Miss Mousie's door, M-hm, M-hm,
   He rode up to Miss Mousie's door,
   Where he'd often been before, M-hm, M-hm.
3. He said, "Miss Mouse, are you within?" . . .
   "Yes, kind sir, I sit and spin." M-hm, M-hm.
4. He took Miss Mouse upon his knee . . .
   Said, "Miss Mouse, will you marry me?" M-hm, M-hm.

5. "Without my Uncle Rat's consent...
   I wouldn't marry the President." M-hm, M-hm.
6. Uncle Rat, he laughed and shook his fat sides...
   To think his niece would be a bride, M-hm, M-hm.
7. Then Uncle Rat rode off to town...
   To buy his niece a wedding gown, M-hm, M-hm.
8. "Oh, where will the wedding supper be?"...
   "Way down yonder in the hollow tree." M-hm, M-hm.
9. The first to come was the little white moth...
   She spread out the tablecloth, M-hm, M-hm.
10. The next to come was the bumblebee...
    Played the fiddle upon his knee, M-hm, M-hm.
11. The next to come was a little flea...
    Danced a jig with the bumblebee, M-hm, M-hm.
12. The next to come was Missus Cow...
    Tried to dance but didn't know how, M-hm, M-hm.
13. Now Mister Frog was dressed in green...
    Sweet Miss Mouse looked like a queen, M-hm, M-hm.
14. In slowly walked the Parson Rook...
    Under his arm he carried a book, M-hm, M-hm.
15. They all gathered round the lucky pair...
    Singing, dancing everywhere, M-hm, M-hm.
16. Then Frog and Mouse went off to France...
    That's the end of my romance, M-hm, M-hm.

GRASSHOPPERS THREE

Suggestion: Can be sung as a three-part round
without accompaniment.

THE BEE AND THE PUP

2. There was a pup-i-up-i-up
   Sat on a bee-i-ee-i-ee,
 Someone went ki-yi-yi-yi-yi,
   And that was he-i-ee-i-ee.

Suggestion: Use various rhythm instruments to accompany parts of the song.

Examples:
V.1 bee - triangle
    wall - drum
    buzz - tambourine
    all - all three instruments
V.2 pup - wood block
    bee - triangle
    ki-yi - cymbals
    he - all five instruments

LITTLE RED CABOOSE

Deke Moffitt

Version 1

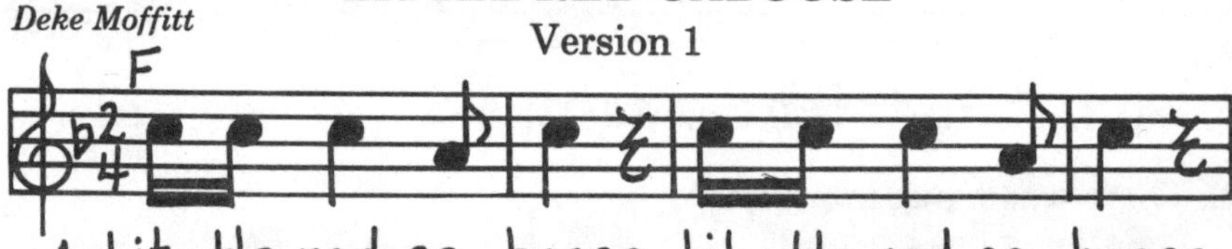

1. Lit-tle red ca-boose, Lit-tle red ca-boose,

Lit-tle red ca-boose be-hind the train, —

Smoke-stack on its back, Com-in' down the track,

Lit-tle red ca-boose be-hind the train. —

2. Little red caboose,
   Little red caboose,
Little red caboose behind the train,
   Coming round the bend,
Hanging on the end,
   Little red caboose behind the train.

2. Little red caboose, chug, chug, chug,
 Little red caboose, chug, chug, chug,
 Little red caboose behind the train, train, train, train,
 Coming round the bend, bend, bend, bend,
 Hanging on the end, end, end, end,
 Little red caboose behind the train.

Suggestion: Versions 1 and 2 can be sung separately or together.

THE BEAR

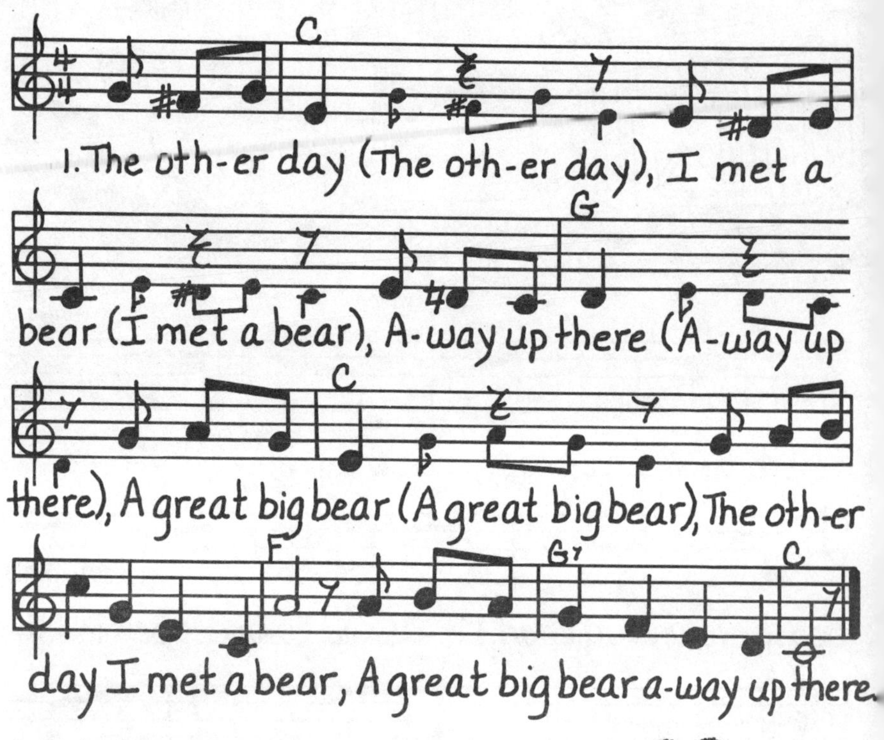

2. He looked at me, (echo),
   I looked at him...
   He sized up me...
   I sized up him...
   He looked at me, I looked at him,
   He sized up me, I sized up him.
3. He said to me...
   "Why don't you run?...
   I see you don't...
   Have any gun,"...
   He said to me, "Why don't you run?
   I see you don't have any gun."
4. And so I ran...
   Away from there...
   And right behind...
   Me was that bear...
   And so I ran away from there,
   And right behind me was that bear.

5. Ahead of me...
   I saw a tree...
   A great big tree...
   Oh, golly gee...
   Ahead of me there was a tree,
   A great big tree, oh, golly gee.
6. The lowest branch...
   Was ten feet up...
   I had to jump...
   And trust my luck...
   The lowest branch was ten feet up,
   I had to jump and trust my luck.
7. And so I jumped...
   Into the air...
   And missed that branch...
   Away up there...
   And so I jumped into the air,
   And missed that branch away up there.
8. Now don't you fret...
   And don't you frown...
   I caught that branch...
   On the way back down...
   Now don't you fret and don't you frown,
   I caught that branch on the way back down.
9. That's all there is...
   There is no more...
   Until I meet...
   That bear once more...
   That's all there is, there is no more
   Until I meet that bear once more.
10. The end, the end...
   The end, the end...
   The end, the end...
   The end, the end...
   The end, the end, the end, the end,
   This time it really is the end!

THE ARKANSAS TRAVELER

David Stephens *Trad. American Reel*

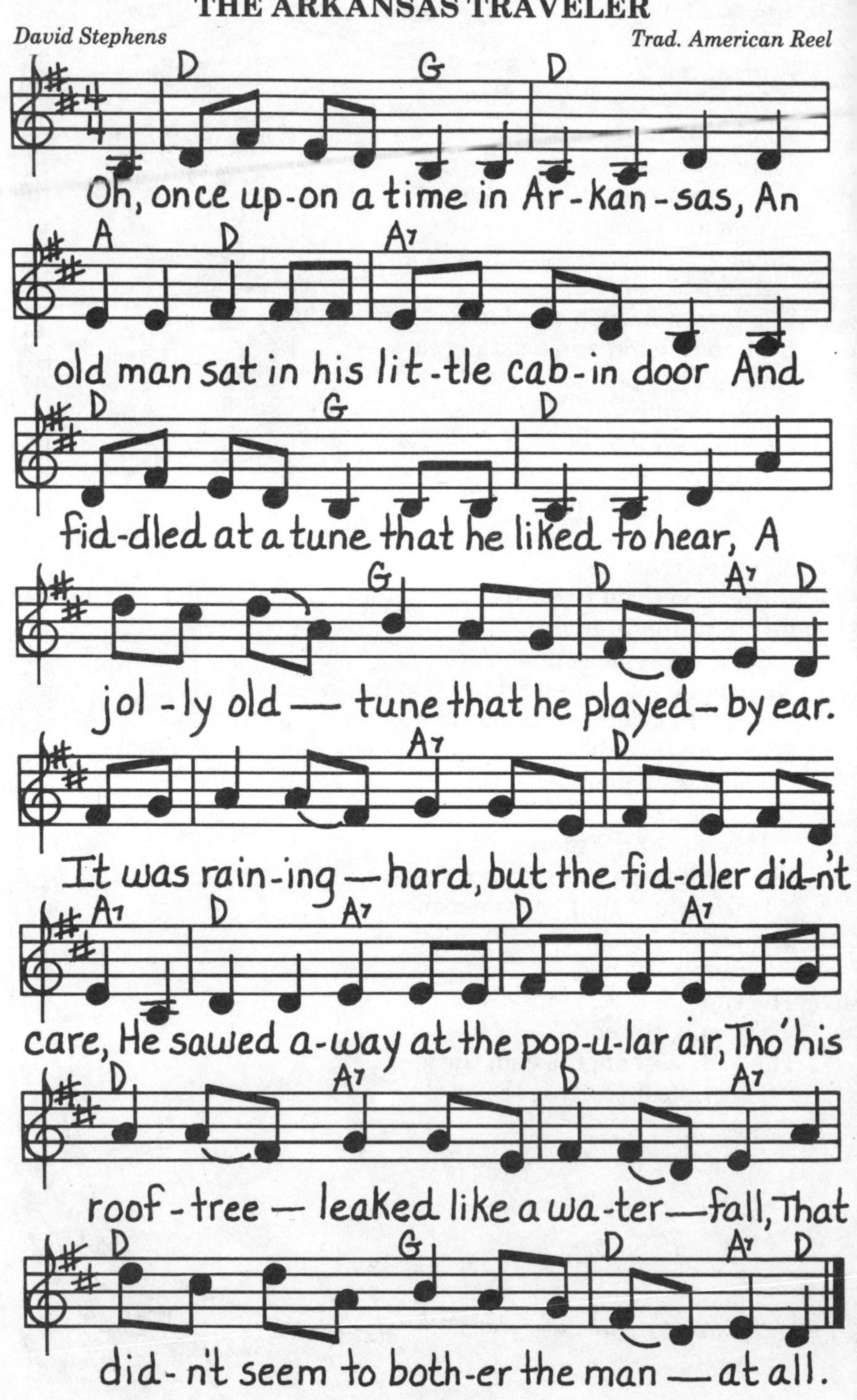

2. A traveler was riding by that day,
   And stopped to hear him a-practicing away;
   The cabin was a-float and his feet were wet,
   But still the old man didn't seem to fret.
   So the stranger said, "Now the way it seems to me,
   You'd better mend your roof," said he.
   But the old man said as he played away,
   "I couldn't mend it now, it's a rainy day."
3. The traveler replied, "That's all quite true,
   But this, I think, is the thing for you to do;
   Get busy on a day that is fair and bright,
   Then patch the old roof till it's good and tight."
   But the old man kept on a-playing at his reel,
   And tapped the ground with his leathery heel.
   "Get along," said he, "for you give me a pain;
   My cabin never leaks when it doesn't rain."

KEEMO KYMO

2. Oh, what you gonna do when the rain don't fall?
   Sing song kitty catcha kymee-oh.
Crops grow small instead of tall,
   Sing song kitty catcha kymee-oh.
      Chorus

GOIN' TO BOSTON

2. Saddle up, girls, and let's go with them,
   Saddle up, girls, and let's go with them,
   Saddle up, girls, and let's go with them,
   Earlye in the mornin'.
   Chorus
3. Get out the way, you'll get run over...
   Chorus

THE RAILROAD CARS ARE COMING

2. The prairie dogs in dogtown
   Will wag each little tail,
They'll think that something's coming,
   Just flying down the rail.
Amid the purple sagebrush,
   The antelope will stand
While railroad cars are coming, humming
   Through the prairie land,
The railroad cars are coming, humming
   Through the prairie land.

OLD DAN TUCKER
Daniel Emmett, 1843
F
1. Come to town the oth-er night, Heard the noise and
Bb F
saw the fight, Watch-man was a-run-nin' round,
Bb
Said, "Old Dan Tuck-er's come to town."
Chorus F Bb C7
So, git out the way, Old Dan Tuck-er, Git out the way,
F Bb
Old Dan Tuck-er, Git out the way, Old Dan Tuck-er,
C7 F
You're too late to come to sup-per.
2. Old Dan Tucker come to town
Ridin' a billygoat, leadin' a hound,
Hound, he barked and the billygoat jumped,
Throwed old Dan, he straddled a stump.
Chorus
3. Old Dan Tucker was a fine old man,
Washed his face in a frying pan,
Combed his hair with a wagon wheel,
And died with a toothache in his heel.
Chorus

HAD A LITTLE ROOSTER
Southern Mountains
1. Had a lit-tle roost-er by the barn-yard gate,
That lit-tle roost-er was my play-mate,
That lit-tle roost-er went cock-a-doo-dle doo, dee
doo-dle-dee, doo-dle-dee, doo-dle-dee-doo.
2. Had a lit-tle cat — by the barn-yard gate,
That lit-tle cat — was my play-mate,

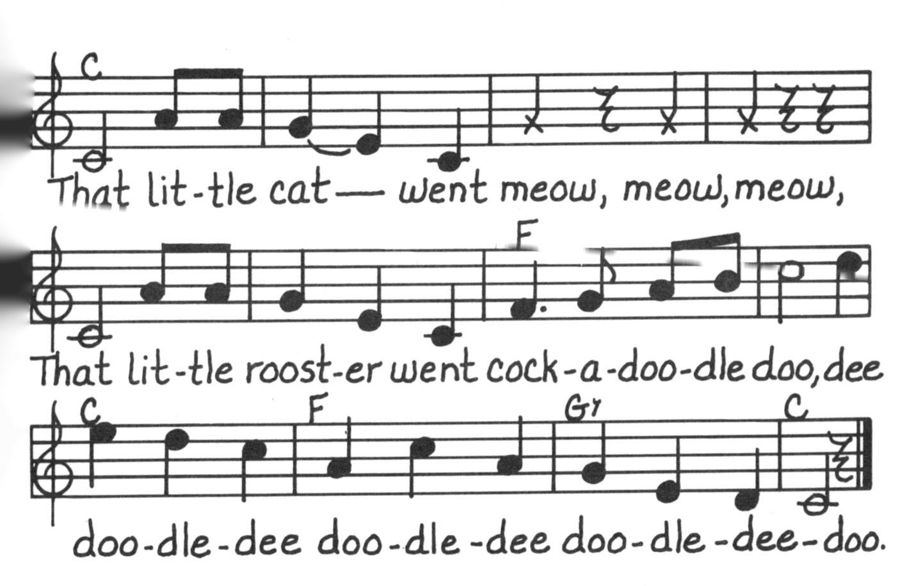

3. Had a little dog by the barnyard gate,
   That little dog was my playmate,
   That little dog went arf, arf, arf,
   That little cat went meow, meow, meow,
   That little rooster went cock-a-doodle doo, dee
   Doodle-dee, doodle-dee, doodle-dee doo.
4. . . .duck went quack, quack, quack. . .
5. . . .pig went oink, oink, oink. . .
6. . . .sheep went baa, baa, baa. . .
7. . . .cow went moo, moo, moo. . .
8. . . .horse went neigh neigh, neigh. . .

LITTLE LIZA JANE

2. Brussels carpet on my floor,
   Little Liza Jane,
   Silver door-plate by my door,
   Little Liza Jane.
   Chorus
3. Come, my love, and be with me...
   Let me take good care of thee...
   Chorus

Suggestion: Sing verse as a call/response. Group sings "Little Liza Jane." All sing chorus.

PUT YOUR LITTLE FOOT

Cowboy Dance

CIRCLE DANCE

Formation: Circle, hands joined.

Action:

[a] Place left toe above and to right of right foot
[b] Sweep it leftward and plant
[c] Slide right foot left to join left foot
[d] Stomp each foot
[e] Place right toe above and to left of left foot
[f] Sweep it rightward and plant
[g] Slide left foot right to join right foot
[h] Walk toward center of circle
[i] Turn to face outward
[j] Walk away from center
[k] Turn to face center

HOP UP, MY LADIES

Virginia

2. Will your horse carry double, Uncle Joe, Uncle Joe?. .
   Chorus
3. Is your horse a single footer, Uncle Joe, Uncle Joe?. .
   Chorus

CIRCLE GAME

Formation: Circle, hands joined.

Action:
[a] Circle left
[b] Circle right
[c] Turn to right, place hands on waist of person in front (Bunny Hop formation)
[d] Hop forward once
[e] Hop backward once
[f] Hop forward three times
[g] Continue Bunny Hop to end

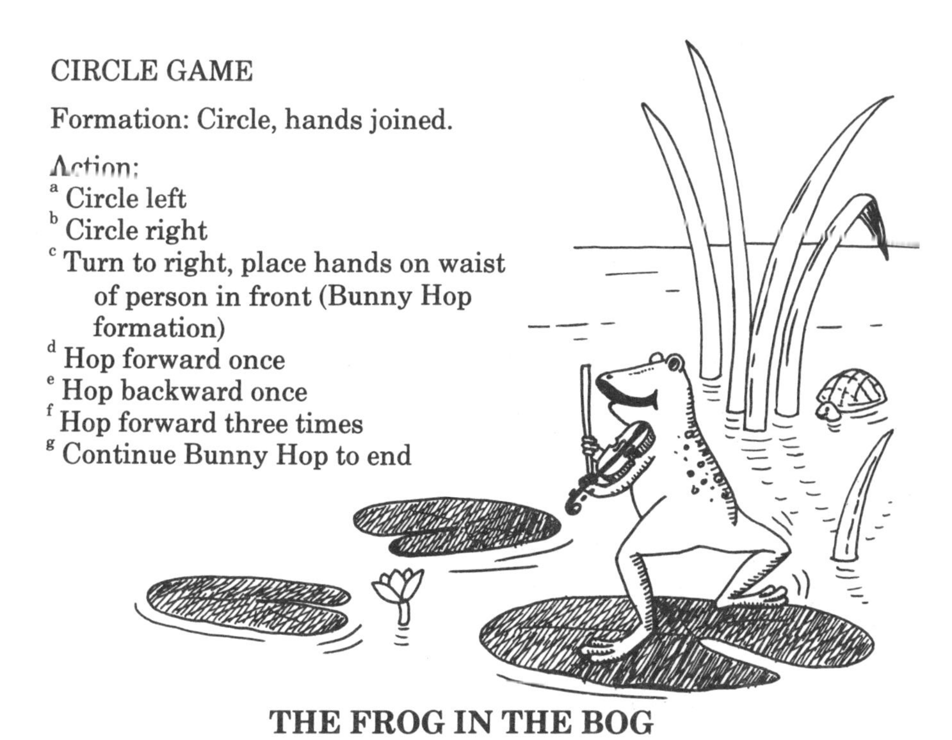

THE FROG IN THE BOG
(Round)

Gertrude Mander *Harvey Worthington Loomis*

2. His music was short for soon he was caught
And now in the middle of the griddle he is frying,
And he's crying, "Rather be drowned.
Rather be drowned."

PAWPAW* PATCH

Kentucky

Where, oh where, is dear lit-tle Nel-lie?

2. Come on, boys, let's go find her,
   Come on, boys, let's go find her,
   Come on, boys, let's go find her,
   Way down yonder in the pawpaw patch.
3. Pickin' up pawpaws, puttin' 'em in your pocket... (3 times)
   Way down yonder in the pawpaw patch.

*** a fruit that looks like a thick, short banana**

SINGING GAME

Formation: Two lines, facing forward, girls on right, boys on left.

Action:

V.1 - Girl in head couple skips left around the boys'line and her own line, returning to place.

V.2 - Boy in head couple leads his line skipping to the right around the girls' line and back to place.

V.3 - Pretend to pick pawpaws as each child in head couple leads his line (girls right, boys left) and meet at end forming an arch with arms raised and hands joined. Couples pass under the arch and return to position with a new head couple. Game continues till all have been head couple.

BUFFALO GALS

Cool White, 1844

An early minstrel song, the title changed depending on the town they were playing — New York Gals, Philadelphia Gals, etc.

2. I stopped her and we had a talk,
   Had a talk, had a talk,
   Her feet took up the whole sidewalk
   And left no room for me.
   Chorus
3. I asked her if she'd have a dance,
   Have a dance, have a dance,
   I thought that I might have a chance
   To shake a foot with her.
   Chorus
4. I danced with a gal with a hole in her stockin'
   And her heel kept a-knockin'
   And her toes kept a-rockin',
   I danced with a gal with a hole in her stockin'
   And we danced by the light of the moon.
   Chorus

CIRCLE DANCE

Formation: Double circle of equal numbers, boys on outside, girls inside.

Action:
V.1 - Girls join hands and circle left. Boys join hands and circle right.
Chorus - Girls touch right hands in center and form a spoke, walking slowly to move wheel. Boys clap in rhythm.
V.2 - Boys and girls nearest each other when wheel stops become partners. Partners face, arms folded out front and walk around each other as in a do-si-do.
Chorus - Same as previous chorus.
V.3 - When wheel stops, new partners join right and left hands and promenade around circle.
Chorus - Same as previous chorus.
V.4 - New partners hook right elbows and swing around for two phrases, then left elbows and swing around for two phrases.
Chorus - Same as previous chorus.

TURN THE GLASSES OVER

English

CIRCLE GAME

Formation: Partners form a double circle, hands crossed and joined in skating position.

Action:

Walk counterclockwise.

Face partner, hands still crossed and joined, raise arms, turn away from each other under arch made by crossed hands. Turn under three times.

Drop hands, inside partners walk clockwise, outside partners walk counterclockwise.

Stop and face new partner.

TURKEY IN THE STRAW

Minstrel Son

2. [a]Went out to milk and I didn't know how,
I milked the goat instead of the cow,
[b]A monkey sittin' on a pile of straw
A-winkin' at his mother-in-law.

Chorus

[i]Turkey in the Straw, (whistle)
[j]Turkey in the Straw, (whistle)
[k]Roll 'em up and twist 'em up a high tuck a-haw,
[l]And hit 'em up a tune called Turkey in the Straw.

. I came to the river and I couldn't get across,
So I paid five dollars for a big bay hoss,
Well, he wouldn't go ahead and he wouldn't stand still,
So he went up and down like an old saw mill.
Chorus

. Did you ever go fishin' on a warm summer day
When all the fish were swimmin' in the bay,
With their hands in their pockets and their pockets in their pants,
Did you ever see a fishie do the Hootchy-Kootchy Dance?
Chorus

CIRCLE GAME

Formation: Single circle of partners, hands joined.

Action: Verse 1
[a] Walk 8 steps to left
[b] Skip 8 to left, then face partner
[c] Clap own hands, clap right hands with partner
[d] Clap own hands, clap left hands with partner
[e] Clap own hands, clap both hands with partner
[f] Clap own hands, slap chest
[g] Join right hands and swing around
[h] Join left hands and swing around

Verse 2
[a] Same as v. 1
[b] Same as v. 1
[i] 4 steps toward center of circle
[j] 4 steps out
[k] Partner on left walks forward 4 steps, partner on right claps
[l] Left partner walks diagonally back 4 steps to new partner. Repeat game for verses 3 and 4.

JINGLE AT THE WINDOW

CIRCLE GAME

Formation: Single circle of partners. Each child has left hand on right shoulder of child in front.

Action:

[a] Walk in circle
[b] Stop walking, partners lock right elbows and swing
[c] Lock left elbows and swing

Repeat several times.

SHOO FLY

CIRCLE GAME
Formation: Circle, hands joined.

Action:
[a] Four steps toward center, raising arms
[b] Four steps backward, lowering arms
[c] Hands still joined, the chosen leader walks directly across to other side and goes under raised, joined hands of two children. Hands still joined, everyone follows the leader through the arch. The circle is now inside out. Repeat song doing the motions backwards until circle is right side out.

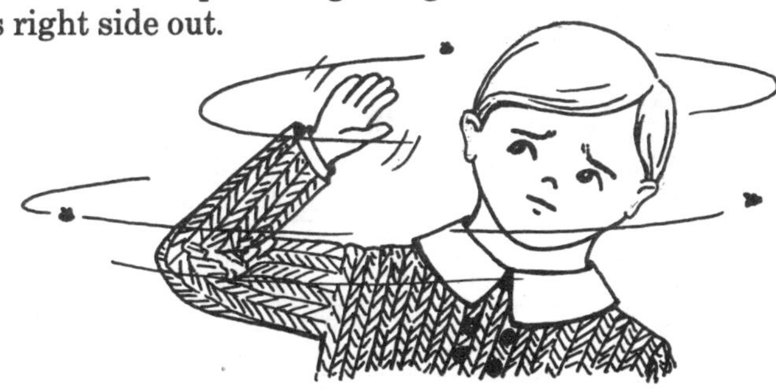

This was a popular nonsense song of the Civil War period.

RIG-A-JIG-JIG

Englis[h]

Suggestion: Walk during verse, skip or gallop during chorus. For extra verses, try skating, running, hopping, tiptoeing, etc. Return to a skip or gallop on the chorus.

INDEX